This journal belongs to

_____

THE *Passion* WITHIN

© 2008 Ellie Claire Gift & Paper Corp.
www.ellieclaire.com

Compiled by Joanie Garborg and Barbara Farmer
Designed by Lisa & Jeff Franke for Lemon Lulu Studios, Minneapolis

Excluding Scripture verses, references to men and masculine pronouns have been
replaced with gender-neutral references.

ISBN 978-1-934770-34-4
Printed in China

THE
Passion
WITHIN

A WOMAN'S JOURNAL

...*inspired by life*

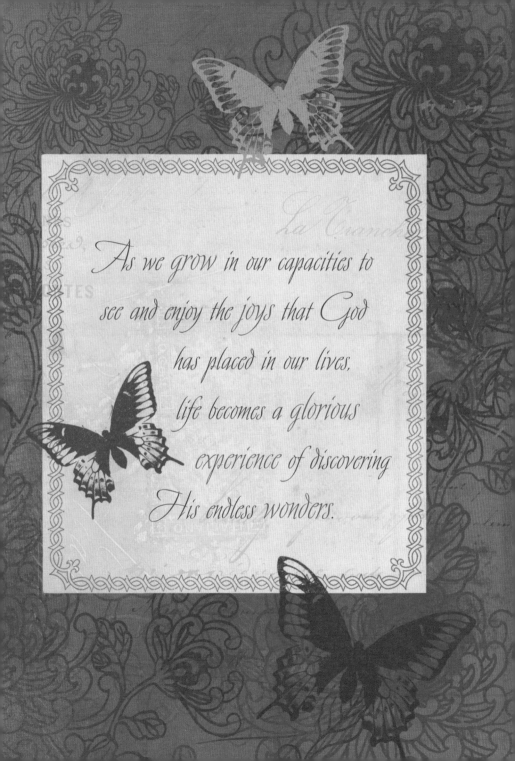

As we grow in our capacities to
see and enjoy the joys that God
has placed in our lives,
life becomes a glorious
experience of discovering
His endless wonders.

To Live with Soul Aflame!

Life is a pure flame, and we live
by an invisible sun within us.

Sir Thomas Browne

Life is no brief candle to me. It is a...splendid torch...
and I want to make it burn as brightly as possible
before handing it over to future generations.

George Bernard Shaw

Fire of God, fire over the earth,
enkindling in our hearts...
Christ Jesus, we want to live,
to live with soul aflame!

Pierre Talec

To Live with Soul Aflame!

....
....
....
....
....
....
....
....
....
....
....
....
....
....

*I ask only one thing from the Lord. This is what I want:
Let me live in the Lord's house all my life. Let me see the Lord's
beauty and look with my own eyes at His Temple.*

PSALM 27:4 NCV

New Life

But God's mercy is great, and He loved us very much.
Though we were spiritually dead because of the things we did
against God, He gave us new life with Christ. You have been
saved by God's grace.... I mean that you have been saved by
grace through believing. You did not save yourselves; it was
a gift from God. It was not the result of your own efforts,
so you cannot brag about it. God has made us what we are.
In Christ Jesus, God made us to do good works,
which God planned in advance for us to live our lives doing.

Ephesians 2:4-5, 8-10 NCV

Since you have been raised to new life with Christ,
set your sights on the realities of heaven, where Christ
sits in the place of honor at God's right hand.

Colossians 3:1-3 NLT

New Life

....

....

....

....

....

....

....

....

....

....

....

....

....

....

....

God puts each fresh morning, each new chance of life,
into our hands as a gift.

The Warmth of Love

Though I have seen the oceans and mountains,
though I have read great books and seen great works
of art, though I have heard symphonies and tasted
the best wines and foods, there is nothing greater
or more beautiful than those people I love.

Christopher de Vinck

Not every day of our lives is overflowing with joy and
celebration. But there are moments when our hearts nearly
burst within us for the sheer joy of being alive. The first sight
of our newborn babies, the warmth of love in another's eyes,
the fresh scent of rain on a hot summer's eve—moments like
these renew in us a heartfelt appreciation for life.

Gwen Ellis

When one has once fully entered the realm of love,
the world—no matter how imperfect—becomes rich and
beautiful, for it consists solely of opportunities for love.

Søren Kierkegaard

The Warmth of Love

All of you should be of one mind. Sympathize with each other. Love each other as brothers and sisters. Be tenderhearted, and keep a humble attitude.

1 PETER 3:8 NLT

Designed on Purpose

All the days ordained for me were written in
Your book before one of them came to be.

Psalm 139:16 NIV

It's in Christ that we find out who we are and what
we are living for. Long before we first heard of Christ
and got our hopes up, He had His eye on us, had designs
on us for glorious living, part of the overall purpose
He is working out in everything and everyone.

Ephesians 1:11-12 THE MESSAGE

To everything there is a season, a time for every
purpose under heaven.

Ecclesiastes 3:1 NKJV

The plans of the Lord stand firm forever, the purposes
of His heart through all generations.

Psalm 33:11 NIV

Designed on Purpose

....

....

....

....

....

....

....

....

....

....

....

....

....

....

....

*The patterns of our days are always rearranging...and each design
for living is unique, graced with its own special beauty.*

Your Whole Heart and Soul

Our prayers should be burning words coming forth
from the furnace of a heart filled with love. Devoutly,
with great sweetness, with natural simplicity,
without any affectation, offer your praise to God
with the whole of your heart and soul.

Mother Teresa

Not a sigh is breathed, not a pain felt, not a grief pierces
the soul, but the throb vibrates to the Father's heart.

Ellen G. White

Let my soul take refuge...beneath the shadow of
Your wings: let my heart, this sea of restless waves,
find peace in You, O God.

Augustine

Your Whole Heart and Soul

···
···
···
···
···
···
···
···
···
···
···
···
···
···
···
···
···
···

My heart is steadfast, O God; I will sing and make music with all my soul....
I will praise You, O Lord, among the nations; I will sing of You among the peoples.

PSALM 108:1-3 NIV

Filled with God's Love

*S*atisfy us in the morning with Your unfailing love,
that we may sing for joy and be glad all our days.

Psalm 90:14 NIV

*B*less the Lord, O my soul;
And all that is within me, bless His holy name!
Bless the Lord, O my soul,
And forget not all His benefits:
Who forgives all your iniquities,
Who heals all your diseases,
Who redeems your life from destruction,
Who crowns you with lovingkindness and tender mercies,
Who satisfies your mouth with good things,
So that your youth is renewed like the eagle's.

Psalm 103:1-5 NKJV

Filled with God's Love

....
....
....
....
....
....
....
....
....
....
....
....
....
....
....
....

God's love is like a river springing up in the Divine Substance and flowing endlessly through His creation, filling all things with life and goodness and strength.

THOMAS MERTON

A Work of Art

Each one of us is God's special work of art. Through us, He teaches and inspires, delights and encourages, informs and uplifts all those who view our lives. God, the master artist, is most concerned about expressing Himself— His thoughts and His intentions—through what He paints in our character.... [He] wants to paint a beautiful portrait of His Son in and through your life. A painting like no other in all of time.

Joni Eareckson Tada

Whether we are poets or parents or teachers or artists or gardeners, we must start where we are and use what we have. In the process of creation and relationship, what seems mundane and trivial may show itself to be holy, precious, part of a pattern.

Luci Shaw

A Work of Art

....

....

....

....

....

....

....

....

....

....

....

....

....

I will give thanks to You, for I am fearfully and wonderfully made;
wonderful are Your works.

PSALM 139:14 NASB

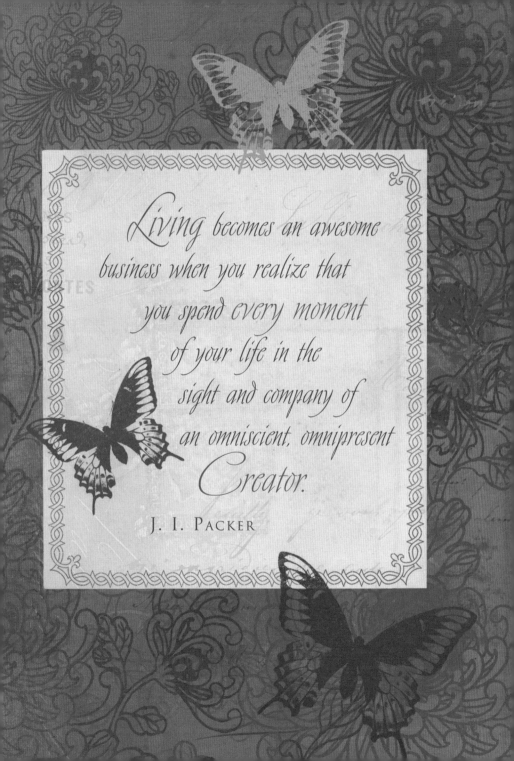

Living becomes an awesome business when you realize that you spend every moment of your life in the sight and company of an omniscient, omnipresent *Creator.*

J. I. PACKER

Good Plans

No eye has seen, no ear has heard,
and no mind has imagined what God
has prepared for those who love Him

1 Corinthians 2:9 NLT

Remember the things I have done in the past.
For I alone am God! I am God, and there is
none like Me. Only I can tell you the future
before it even happens. Everything I plan will
come to pass, for I do whatever I wish.

Isaiah 46:9-10 NLT

"For I know the plans I have for you," declares
the Lord, "plans to prosper you and not to
harm you, plans to give you hope and a future."

Jeremiah 29:11 NIV

Good Plans

....

....

....

....

....

....

....

....

....

....

....

....

....

....

Every person's life is a fairy tale written by God's fingers.

HANS CHRISTIAN ANDERSEN

A Reflection of Your Soul

What glows from the inside often reflects
what is on the outside.

Christopher de Vinck

The beauty of a woman is not in a facial mole,
But true beauty in a woman is reflected in her soul.
It is the caring that she lovingly gives, the passion that she shows,
And the beauty of a woman with passing years—only grows!

Audrey Hepburn

Expressed affection is the best of all methods
to use when you want to light a glow in someone's
heart and to feel it in your own.

Ruth Stafford Peale

A Reflection of Your Soul

....

....

....

....

....

....

....

....

....

....

....

....

....

....

So all of us who have had that veil removed can see and reflect the glory of the Lord. And the Lord—who is the Spirit—makes us more and more like Him as we are changed into His glorious image.

2 CORINTHIANS 3:18 NIV

At Home in God's House

Remain in Me, and I will remain in you. A branch
cannot produce fruit alone but must remain in the vine....
If you remain in Me and follow My teachings,
you can ask anything you want, and it will be given to you.
You should produce much fruit and show that you are
My followers, which brings glory to My Father. I loved
you as the Father loved Me. Now remain in My love.

John 15:4, 7-9 NCV

Ask, and it will be given to you; seek, and you
will find; knock, and it will be opened to you.
For everyone who asks, receives; and he who seeks, finds;
and to him who knocks, it will be opened.

Luke 11:9-10 NASB

At Home in God's House

After a hard day scrambling to find your way around the world, it's assuring
to come home to a place you know. God can be equally familiar to you....
Just as your earthly house is a place of refuge, so God's house is a place of peace.

MAX LUCADO

Faith Adventure

There will always be the unknown. There will always be the unprovable. But faith confronts those frontiers with a thrilling leap. Then life becomes vibrant with adventure!

Robert Schuller

Faith means you want God and want to want nothing else....
In faith there is movement and development.
Each day something is new.

Brennan Manning

A little faith will bring your soul to heaven,
but a lot of faith will bring heaven to your soul.

Dwight L. Moody

Faith is not a sense, not sight, not reason,
but a taking God at His Word.

Evans

Faith Adventure

....

....

....

....

....

....

....

....

....

....

....

....

....

For with God all things are possible.

MARK 10:27 NKJV

Renewing Word

You're my place of quiet retreat;
I wait for Your Word to renew me.

Psalm 119:114 THE MESSAGE

You have dealt well with Your servant,
O Lord, according to Your word.
Teach me good judgment and knowledge,
For I believe in Your commandments.
Before I was afflicted I went astray,
But now I keep Your word.
You are good, and do good;
Teach me Your statutes.

Psalm 119:65-68 NKJV

All Your words are true;
all Your righteous laws are eternal.

Psalm 119:160 NIV

Renewing Word

....

....

....

....

....

....

....

....

....

....

....

....

....

....

....

Be still, and in the quiet moments, listen to the voice of your heavenly Father.
His words can renew your spirit...no one knows you and your needs like He does.

JANET L. WEAVER SMITH

A Sense of Wonder

Whether sixty or sixteen, there is in every human
being's heart the love of wonder, the sweet amazement
at the stars and starlike things, the undaunted challenge
of events, the unfailing childlike appetite for what-next,
and the joy of the game of living.

Samuel Ullman

Loving Creator, help me reawaken my childlike sense
of wonder at the delights of Your world!

Marilyn Morgan Helleberg

Dear Lord, grant me the grace of wonder. Surprise me,
amaze me, awe me in every crevice of Your universe....
Each day enrapture me with Your marvelous things
without number. I do not ask to see the reason for it all;
I ask only to share the wonder of it all.

Abraham Joshua Heschel

A Sense of Wonder

....

....

....

....

....

....

....

....

....

....

....

....

....

....

I will give thanks to the Lord with all my heart;
I will tell of all Your wonders.

PSALM 9:1 NASB

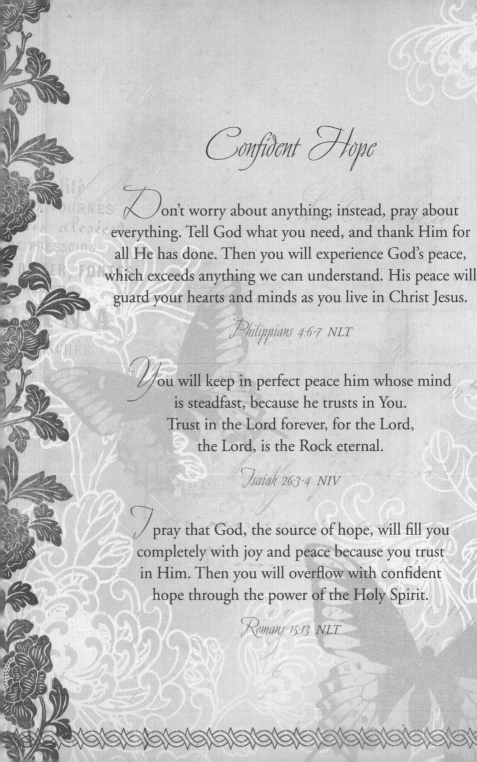

Confident Hope

Don't worry about anything; instead, pray about everything. Tell God what you need, and thank Him for all He has done. Then you will experience God's peace, which exceeds anything we can understand. His peace will guard your hearts and minds as you live in Christ Jesus.

Philippians 4:6-7 NLT

You will keep in perfect peace him whose mind is steadfast, because he trusts in You. Trust in the Lord forever, for the Lord, the Lord, is the Rock eternal.

Isaiah 26:3-4 NIV

I pray that God, the source of hope, will fill you completely with joy and peace because you trust in Him. Then you will overflow with confident hope through the power of the Holy Spirit.

Romans 15:13 NLT

Confident Hope

....

....

....

....

....

....

....

....

....

....

....

....

....

....

....

....

*Trust is giving up what little I have in strength and power
so I can confidently relax in His power and strength.*

GLORIA GAITHER

Within each of us there is
an inner place where the living
God Himself
longs to dwell,
our sacred center
of belief.

God Draws Near

When you are lonely I wish you love;
When you are down I wish you joy;
When you are troubled I wish you peace;
When things are complicated I wish you simple beauty;
When things are chaotic I wish you inner silence;
When things seem empty I wish you hope,
And the sweet sense of God's presence every passing day.

God still draws near to us in the ordinary,
commonplace, everyday experiences and places....
He comes in surprising ways.

Henry Gariepy

God Draws Near

....

....

....

....

....

....

....

....

....

....

....

....

....

....

*I have set the Lord always before me; because He is at
my right hand I shall not be moved.*

PSALM 16:8 NKJV

The Garden of My Life

At that same time, a fine vineyard will appear.
There's something to sing about! I, God, tend it.
I keep it well-watered. I keep careful watch over it so
that no one can damage it.... Even if it gives Me
thistles and thornbushes, I'll just pull them out
and burn them up. Let that vine cling to Me
for safety, let it find a good and whole life with Me,
let it hold on for a good and whole life.

Isaiah 27:2-5 THE MESSAGE

The Lord will guide you always; He will satisfy
your needs in a sun-scorched land and will
strengthen your frame. You will be like a well-watered
garden, like a spring whose waters never fail.

Isaiah 58:11 NIV

The Garden of My Life

....

....

....

....

....

....

....

....

....

....

....

....

....

....

It is God's knowledge of me, His careful husbanding of the ground of my being,
His constant presence in the garden of my little life that guarantees my joy.

W. PHILLIP KELLER

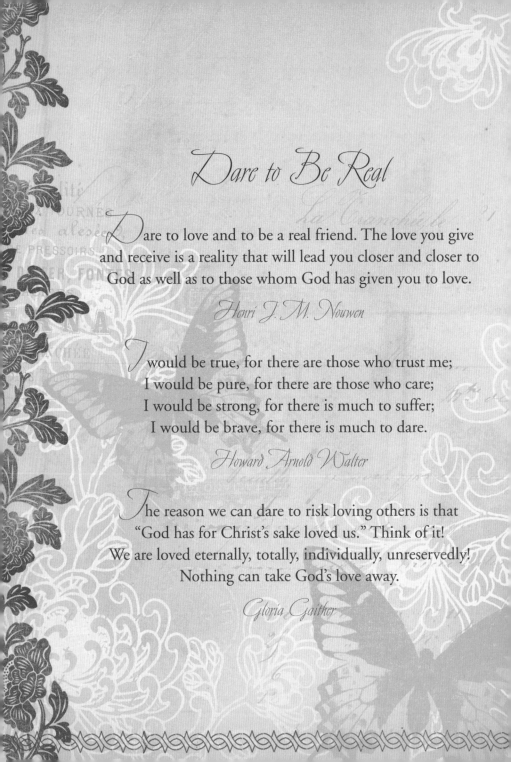

Dare to Be Real

Dare to love and to be a real friend. The love you give and receive is a reality that will lead you closer and closer to God as well as to those whom God has given you to love.

Henri J. M. Nouwen

I would be true, for there are those who trust me;
I would be pure, for there are those who care;
I would be strong, for there is much to suffer;
I would be brave, for there is much to dare.

Howard Arnold Walter

The reason we can dare to risk loving others is that
"God has for Christ's sake loved us." Think of it!
We are loved eternally, totally, individually, unreservedly!
Nothing can take God's love away.

Gloria Gaither

Dare to Be Real

....
....
....
....
....
....
....
....
....
....
....
....
....
....
....

Don't just pretend to love others. Really love them. Hate what is wrong.
Hold tightly to what is good. Love each other with genuine affection,
and take delight in honoring each other.

ROMANS 12:9-10 NLT

Made for Joy

Our hearts were made for joy. Our hearts were made
to enjoy the One who created them. Too deeply planted
to be much affected by the ups and downs of life,
this joy is a knowing and a being known by our Creator.
He sets our hearts alight with radiant joy.

If one is joyful, it means that one is faithfully
living for God, and that nothing else counts;
and if one gives joy to others one is doing God's work.
With joy without and joy within, all is well.

Janet Erskine Stuart

Live for today but hold your hands open to tomorrow.
Anticipate the future and its changes with joy. There is a
seed of God's love in every event, every circumstance,
every unpleasant situation in which you may find yourself.

Barbara Johnson

Made for Joy

The joy of the Lord is your strength.

God's Thoughts

Your thoughts—how rare, how beautiful! God, I'll never comprehend them! I couldn't even begin to count them— any more than I could count the sand of the sea. Oh, let me rise in the morning and live always with You!

Psalm 139:17-18 THE MESSAGE

How great are Your works, O Lord, how profound Your thoughts!

Psalm 92:5 NIV

The Lord is the everlasting God, the Creator of all the earth. He never grows weak or weary. No one can measure the depths of His understanding.... Even youths will become weak and tired, and young men will fall in exhaustion. But those who trust in the Lord will find new strength. They will soar high on wings like eagles. They will run and not grow weary. They will walk and not faint.

Isaiah 40:28, 30-31 NLT

God's Thoughts

Just when we least expect it, [God] intrudes into our neat
and tidy notions about who He is and how He works.

JONI EARECKSON TADA

Listen to Your Life

Listen to your life. See it for the fathomless mystery that it is. In the boredom and pain of it no less than in the excitement and gladness: touch, taste, smell your way to the holy and hidden heart of it because in the last analysis all moments are key moments and life itself is grace.

Frederick Buechner

See each morning a world made anew, as if it were the morning of the very first day;...treasure and use it, as if it were the final hour of the very last day.

Fay Hartzell Arnold

Walk softly. Speak tenderly. Love fervently.

Listen to Your Life

Let us make sure that we do not just hold it as an idea in our heads or a sentiment in our hearts, but work out its implications in every detail of our lives.

GALATIANS 5:25 THE MESSAGE

My Hope Comes from Him

The Lord delights in those who fear Him,
who put their hope in His unfailing love.

Psalm 147:11 NIV

Be of good courage,
And He shall strengthen your heart,
All you who hope in the Lord.

Psalm 31:24 NKJV

Hope does not disappoint, because the love of God
has been poured out in our hearts by the Holy Spirit
who was given to us.

Romans 5:5 NKJV

Find rest, O my soul, in God alone;
my hope comes from Him.
He alone is my rock and my salvation;
He is my fortress, I will not be shaken.

Psalm 62:5-6 NIV

My Hope Comes from Him

*Hope is not a granted wish or a favor performed;
no, it is far greater than that. It is a zany, unpredictable dependence
on a God who loves to surprise us out of our socks.*

MAX LUCADO

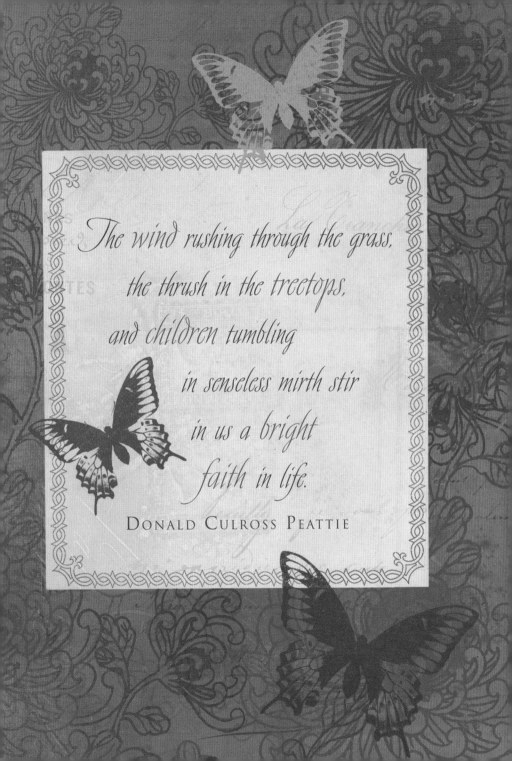

The wind rushing through the grass,
the thrush in the treetops,
and children tumbling
in senseless mirth stir
in us a bright
faith in life.

DONALD CULROSS PEATTIE

Full of Laughter

Teach me, Father, to value each day, to live,
to love, to laugh, to play.

Kathi Mills

Wholehearted, ready laughter heals, encourages,
relaxes anyone within hearing distance. The laughter
that springs from love makes wide the space
around it—gives room for the loved one to enter in.
Real laughter welcomes, and never shuts out.

Eugenia Price

Sense of humor; God's great gift
causes spirits to uplift,
Helps to make our bodies mend;
lightens burdens; cheers a friend;
Tickles children; elders grin
at this warmth that glows within;
Surely in the great hereafter
heaven must be full of laughter!

It is often just as sacred to laugh as it is to pray.

Charles R. Swindoll

Full of Laughter

....
....
....
....
....
....
....
....
....
....
....
....
....
....
....

He will yet fill your mouth with laughter
and your lips with shouts of joy.

JOB 8:21 NIV

Love Like That

Watch what God does, and then you do it,
like children who learn proper behavior from their parents.
Mostly what God does is love you. Keep company
with Him and learn a life of love. Observe how Christ
loved us. His love was not cautious but extravagant.
He didn't love in order to get something from us but to
give everything of Himself to us. Love like that.

Ephesians 5:1-2 THE MESSAGE

I pray that your love will overflow more and more,
and that you will keep on growing in your
knowledge and understanding.

Philippians 1:9 NLT

Love Like That

....

....

....

....

....

....

....

....

....

....

....

....

....

*Open your hearts to the love God instills.... God loves you tenderly.
What He gives you is not to be kept under lock and key, but to be shared.*

MOTHER TERESA

In the Presence of God

Just slipping quietly into the presence of God can be
so exotic and fresh that it delights us enormously.

Richard J. Foster

O the pure delight of a single hour
that before Thy throne I spend,
When I kneel in prayer, and with Thee, my God,
I commune as friend with friend!

Fanny J. Crosby

The Lord's chief desire is to reveal Himself to you and,
in order for Him to do that, He gives you abundant grace.
The Lord gives you the experience of enjoying His presence.
He touches you, and His touch is so delightful that,
more than ever, you are drawn inwardly to Him.

Madame Jeanne Guyon

In the Presence of God

....
....
....
....
....
....
....
....
....
....
....
....
....
....
....

Happy are those who hear the joyful call to worship,
for they will walk in the light of Your presence, Lord.

PSALM 89:15 NLT

Simply Be Yourself

*Y*ou're blessed when you're content with just
who you are—no more, no less. That's the
moment you find yourselves proud owners of
everything that can't be bought.

Matthew 5:5 THE MESSAGE

*D*o you want to stand out? Then step down.
Be a servant. If you puff yourself up, you'll get the wind
knocked out of you. But if you're content to simply
be yourself, your life will count for plenty.

Matthew 23:11 THE MESSAGE

*C*ome to Me, all you who are weary and burdened,
and I will give you rest. Take My yoke upon you
and learn from Me, for I am gentle and humble in heart,
and you will find rest for your souls. For My yoke is
easy and My burden is light.

Matthew 11:28-30 NIV

Simply Be Yourself

....

....

....

....

....

....

....

....

....

....

....

....

....

Be patient with yourself and others. There are no shortcuts to spirituality. Growing fruit takes time.

You're Indispensable

God has a wonderful plan for each person He has chosen.
He knew even before He created this world what beauty
He would bring forth from our lives.

Louis B. Wyly

Everyone has a unique role to fill in the world and is
important in some respect. Everyone, including and
perhaps especially you, is indispensable.

Nathaniel Hawthorne

God gives us all gifts, special abilities that we are entrusted
with developing to help serve Him and serve others.

You're Indispensable

Each of you has received a gift to use to serve others.
Be good servants of God's various gifts of grace.

1 PETER 4:10 NCV

A Personal Guide

I'll take the hand of those who don't know the way,
who can't see where they're going. I'll be a personal
guide to them, directing them through unknown country.
I'll be right there to show them what roads to take,
make sure they don't fall into the ditch. These are
the things I'll be doing for them—sticking with them,
not leaving them for a minute.

Isaiah 42:16 THE MESSAGE

Whether you turn to the right or to the left,
your ears will hear a voice behind you, saying,
"This is the way; walk in it."

Isaiah 30:21 NIV

We can make our plans, but the Lord
determines our steps.

Proverbs 16:9 NLT

A Personal Guide

*Heaven often seems distant and unknown, but if He who made the road...
is our guide, we need not fear to lose the way.*

HENRY VAN DYKE

The Light of Love

Love is a flame which burns in heaven, and whose
soft reflections radiate to us.... It is by love that we double
our being; it is by love that we approach God.

Aimee Martin

A joyful heart is like a sunshine of God's love,
the hope of eternal happiness, a burning flame
of God.... And if we pray, we will become that
sunshine of God's love—in our own home,
the place where we live, and in the world at large.

Mother Teresa

Love is indestructible;
Its holy flame forever burneth;
From heaven it came,
to earth returneth.

Robert Southey

The Light of Love

God, Your love is so precious! You protect people in the shadow of Your wings....
You are the giver of life. Your light lets us enjoy life.

PSALM 36:7, 9 NCV

Love is the only passion
which includes in
its dreams the
happiness
of someone else.

KARR

The Last Shall Be First

Serve each other in humility, for "God opposes
the proud but favors the humble." So humble
yourselves under the mighty power of God,
and at the right time He will lift you up in honor.

1 Peter 5:5-6 NLT

Whoever wishes to become great among you
shall be your servant, and whoever wishes to be
first among you shall be your slave; just as
the Son of Man did not come to be served,
but to serve, and to give His life a ransom for many.

Matthew 20:26-28 NASB

If your gift is serving others, serve them well.

Romans 12:7 NLT

The Last Shall Be First

....

....

....

....

....

....

....

....

....

....

....

....

....

....

*If we fully comprehended the brevity of life, our greatest desire
would be to please God and to serve one another.*

JAMES DOBSON

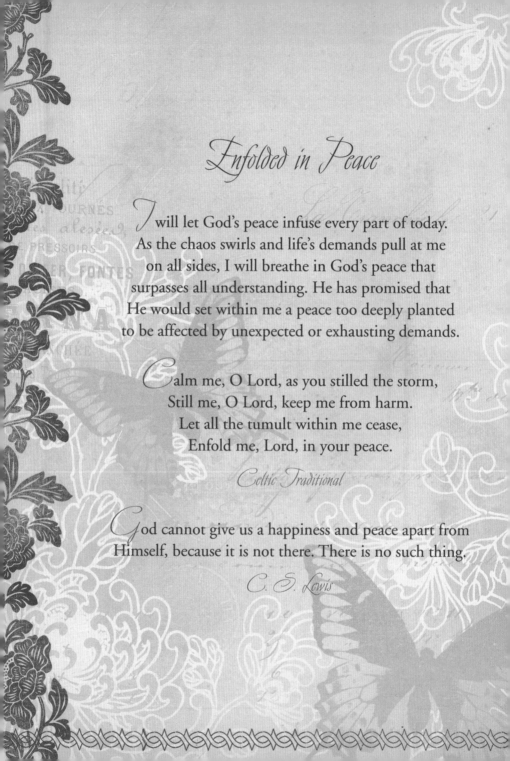

Enfolded in Peace

I will let God's peace infuse every part of today.
As the chaos swirls and life's demands pull at me
on all sides, I will breathe in God's peace that
surpasses all understanding. He has promised that
He would set within me a peace too deeply planted
to be affected by unexpected or exhausting demands.

Calm me, O Lord, as you stilled the storm,
Still me, O Lord, keep me from harm.
Let all the tumult within me cease,
Enfold me, Lord, in your peace.

Celtic Traditional

God cannot give us a happiness and peace apart from
Himself, because it is not there. There is no such thing.

C. S. Lewis

Enfolded in Peace

....

....

....

....

....

....

....

....

....

....

....

....

....

....

*Because of the tender mercy of our God, with which the Sunrise
from on high will visit us, to shine upon those who sit in darkness...
to guide our feet into the way of peace.*

LUKE 1:78-79 NASB

God Is Our Refuge

Hear my cry, O God; Give heed to my prayer.
From the end of the earth I call to You when my
heart is faint; Lead me to the rock that is
higher than I. For You have been a refuge for me,
A tower of strength against the enemy.
Let me dwell in Your tent forever;
Let me take refuge in the shelter of Your wings.

Psalm 61:1-4 NASB

Whom have I in heaven but You?
And besides You, I desire nothing on earth.
My flesh and my heart may fail,
But God is the strength of my
heart and my portion forever....
As for me, the nearness of God is my good;
I have made the Lord God my refuge.

Psalm 73:25-26, 28 NASB

God Is Our Refuge

....

....

....

....

....

....

....

....

....

....

....

....

....

When God has become...our refuge and our fortress, then we can reach out to Him in the midst of a broken world and feel at home while still on the way.

HENRI J. M. NOUWEN

The Wild Joys of Living

God created us with an overwhelming desire to soar.
Our desire to develop and use every ounce of
potential He's placed in us is not egotistical.
He designed us to be tremendously productive and
"to mount up with wings like eagles," realistically
dreaming of what He can do with our potential.

Carol Kent

Oh, the wild joys of living!
The leaping from rock up to rock...
How good is man's life, the mere living!
How fit to employ
All the heart and the soul
and the senses forever in joy!

Robert Browning

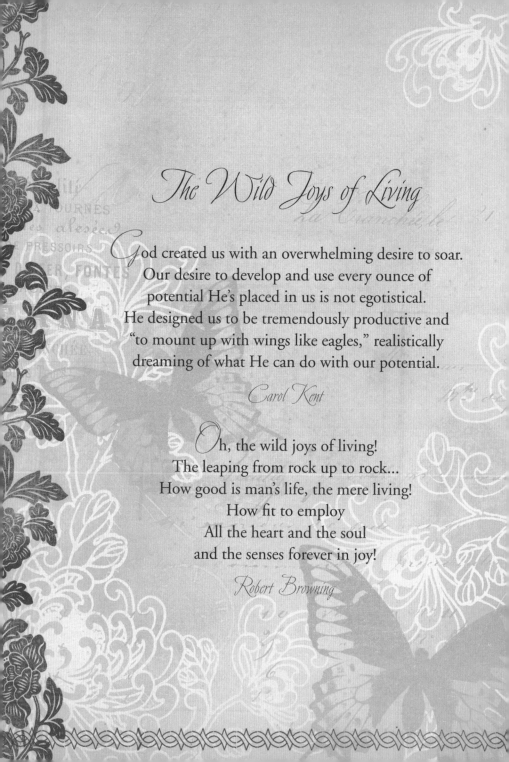

The Wild Joys of Living

....

....

....

....

....

....

....

....

....

....

....

....

....

....

Christ's love has moved me to such extremes. His love has
the first and last word in everything we do.

2 CORINTHIANS 5:13 THE MESSAGE

The Beauty of Dreams

We grow great by dreams.... [We] see things in
the soft haze of a spring day or in the red fire of
a long winter's evening. Some of us let these great
dreams die, but others nourish and protect them;
nurse them through bad days till they bring them to
the sunshine and light, which comes always to those
who sincerely hope that their dreams will come true.

Woodrow Wilson

The future belongs to those who believe in
the beauty of their dreams.

Eleanor Roosevelt

A thing of beauty is a joy forever:
Its loveliness increases; it will never
Pass into nothingness; but still will keep
A bower quiet for us, and a sleep
Full of sweet dreams...
An endless fountain of immortal drink,
Pouring unto us from the heaven's brink.

John Keats

God gives us dreams so we'll long for His reality.

Beth Moore

The Beauty of Dreams

....

....

....

....

....

....

....

....

....

....

....

....

....

....

Trust steadily in God, hope unswervingly, love extravagantly.

1 CORINTHIANS 13:13 THE MESSAGE

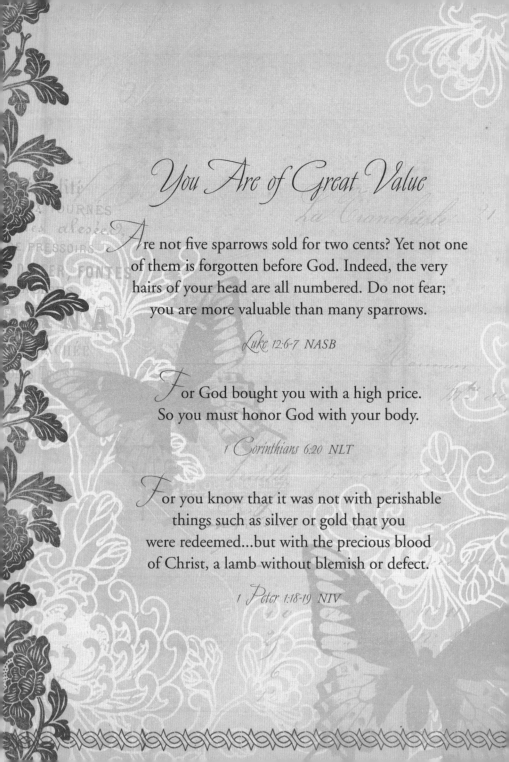

You Are of Great Value

Are not five sparrows sold for two cents? Yet not one of them is forgotten before God. Indeed, the very hairs of your head are all numbered. Do not fear; you are more valuable than many sparrows.

Luke 12:6-7 NASB

For God bought you with a high price. So you must honor God with your body.

1 Corinthians 6:20 NLT

For you know that it was not with perishable things such as silver or gold that you were redeemed...but with the precious blood of Christ, a lamb without blemish or defect.

1 Peter 1:18-19 NIV

You Are of Great Value

You are in the Beloved...therefore infinitely dear to the Father, unspeakably precious to Him.

NORMAN F. DOWTY

Like Supernatural Effervescence

Love wholeheartedly, be surprised, give thanks and praise—
then you will discover the fullness of your life.

David Steindl-Rast

The thought of You stirs us so deeply that we cannot be
content unless we praise You, because You have made us for
Yourself and our hearts find no peace until they rest in You.

Augustine

Like supernatural effervescence, praise will sometimes
bubble up from the joy of simply knowing Christ. Praise
like that is...delight. Pure pleasure! But praise can also be
supernatural determination. A decisive action. Praise like
that is...quiet resolve. Fixed devotion. Strength of spirit.

Like Supernatural Effervescence

From the fullness of His grace we have all
received one blessing after another.

JOHN 1:16 NIV

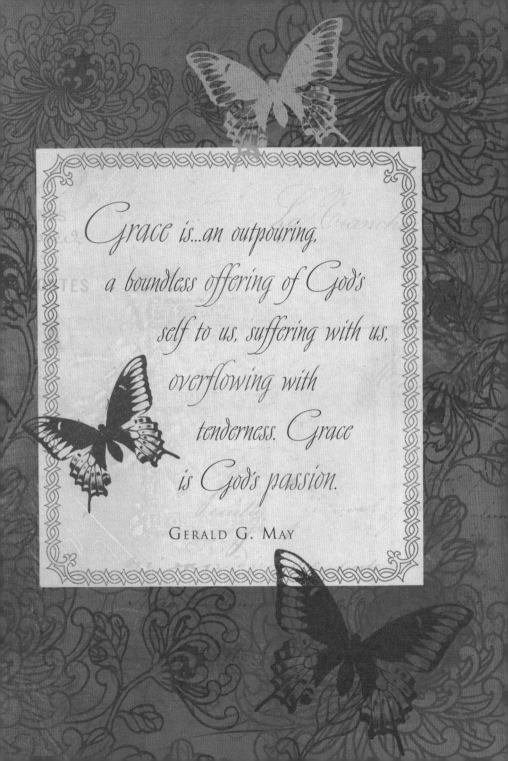

Grace is...an outpouring,
a boundless offering of God's
self to us, suffering with us,
overflowing with
tenderness. Grace
is God's passion.

GERALD G. MAY

Live by Grace

The name of our Lord Jesus will be honored because of the way you live, and you will be honored along with Him. This is all made possible because of the grace of our God and Lord, Jesus Christ.

2 Thessalonians 1:12 nlt

I have been crucified with Christ and I no longer live, but Christ lives in me. The life I live in the body, I live by faith in the Son of God, who loved me and gave Himself for me.

Galatians 2:20 niv

For it is by grace you have been saved, through faith— and this not from yourselves, it is the gift of God— not by works, so that no one can boast.

Ephesians 2:8-9 niv

Live by Grace

....

....

....

....

....

....

....

....

....

....

....

....

....

....

....

....

....

Faith is the centerpiece of a connected life. It allows us to live by the grace of invisible strands. It is a belief in a wisdom superior to our own.

TERRY TEMPEST WILLIAMS

The Little Things

It's the little things we do and say
That mean so much as we go our way.
A kindly deed can lift a load
From weary shoulders on the road.

A gentle word, like summer rain,
May soothe some heart and banish pain.
What joy or sadness often springs
From just the simple little things!

Willa Hooy

Don't ever let yourself get so busy that you miss those
little but important extras in life—the beauty of a day...
the smile of a friend...the serenity of a quiet moment alone.
For it is often life's smallest pleasures and gentlest joys
that make the biggest and most lasting difference.

It's the little things that make up the richest part
of the tapestry of our lives.

The Little Things

He won't brush aside the bruised and the hurt and He won't disregard
the small and insignificant, but He'll steadily and firmly set things right.

ISAIAH 42:3 THE MESSAGE

God's Care

The Lord is my shepherd;
I shall not want.
He makes me to lie down in green pastures;
He leads me beside the still waters.
He restores my soul;
He leads me in the paths of righteousness
For His name's sake.
Yea, though I walk through the valley of the shadow of death,
I will fear no evil;
For You are with me;
Your rod and Your staff, they comfort me.
You prepare a table before me in the presence of my enemies;
You anoint my head with oil;
My cup runs over.
Surely goodness and mercy shall follow me
All the days of my life;
And I will dwell in the house of the Lord
Forever.

Psalm 23:1-6 NKJV

God's Care

....

....

....

....

....

....

....

....

....

....

....

....

....

....

....

God never abandons anyone on whom He has set His love; nor does Christ, the good shepherd, ever lose track of His sheep.

J. I. PACKER

The Inner Sanctuary of the Soul

Deep within us all there is an amazing inner sanctuary
of the soul, a holy place...to which we may continuously
return. Eternity is at our hearts, pressing upon our
time-torn lives, warming us...calling us home unto Itself.
Yielding to these persuasions...utterly and completely,
to the Light within, is the beginning of true life.

Thomas R. Kelly

There is no event so commonplace but that God is
present within it, always hiddenly, always leaving
you room to recognize Him or not to recognize Him,
but all the more fascinatingly because of that,
all the more compellingly and hauntingly.

Frederick Buechner

My Lord, You have heard the cry of my heart because
it was You who cried out within my heart.

Thomas Merton

The Inner Sanctuary of the Soul

....

....

....

....

....

....

....

....

....

....

....

....

....

....

How lovely are Your dwelling places, O Lord of hosts!
My soul longed and even yearned for the courts of the Lord.

PSALM 84:1-2 NASB

Dreams Fulfilled

Lift up your eyes. Your heavenly Father waits
to bless you—in inconceivable ways to make your life
what you never dreamed it could be.

Anne Ortlund

The human heart, has hidden treasures,
In secret kept, in silence sealed;—
The thoughts, the hopes, the dreams, the pleasures,
Whose charms were broken if revealed.

Charlotte Brontë

Far away, there in the sunshine, are my highest aspirations.
I may not reach them but I can look up and see their beauty,
believe in them, and try to follow where they lead.

Louisa May Alcott

Dreams Fulfilled

I'll lead you to buried treasures, secret caches of valuables—
Confirmations that it is, in fact, I, God...who calls you by your name.

ISAIAH 45:3 THE MESSAGE

Love One Another

Clothe yourselves with compassion, kindness, humility, gentleness and patience. Bear with each other and forgive whatever grievances you may have against one another. Forgive as the Lord forgave you. And over all these virtues put on love, which binds them all together in perfect unity.

Colossians 3:12-14 NIV

Never walk away from someone who deserves help; your hand is God's hand for that person.

Proverbs 3:27 THE MESSAGE

May the patience and encouragement that come from God allow you to live in harmony with each other.

Romans 15:5 NCV

Love One Another

....

....

....

....

....

....

....

....

....

....

....

....

....

....

....

*In God's wisdom, He frequently chooses to meet our needs by showing
His love toward us through the hands and hearts of others.*

JACK HAYFORD

Friends Given by God

Friends given by God in mercy and in love;
My counsellors, my comforters, and guides;
My joy in grief, my second bliss in joy;
Companions of my young desires; in doubt
My oracles; my wings in high pursuit.
O, I remember, and will ne'er forget
Our meeting spots, our chosen sacred hours,
Our burning words, that utter'd all the soul,
Our faces beaming with unearthly love;
Sorrow with sorrow sighing, hope with hope
Exulting, heart embracing heart entire.

Sir Frederick Pollock

The friend given you by circumstances over which
you have no control was God's own gift.

Frederick Robertson

Friends Given by God

....

....

....

....

....

....

....

....

....

....

....

....

....

....

Friends come and friends go, but a true friend sticks by you like family.

PROVERBS 18:22 THE MESSAGE

Love the Lord God with all your passion and prayer and intelligence and energy.

MARK 12:29 THE MESSAGE

Live Carefree Before God

Be content with who you are, and don't put on airs. God's strong hand is on you; He'll promote you at the right time. Live carefree before God; He is most careful with you.

1 Peter 5:6-7 THE MESSAGE

I know what it is to be in need, and I know what it is to have plenty. I have learned the secret of being content in any and every situation.... I can do everything through Him who gives me strength.

Philippians 4:12-13 NIV

Now godliness with contentment is great gain. For we brought nothing into this world, and it is certain we can carry nothing out. And having food and clothing, with these we shall be content.

1 Timothy 6:6-8 NKJV

Live Carefree Before God

God takes care of His own. He knows our needs. He anticipates our crises. He is moved by our weaknesses. He stands ready to come to our rescue. And at just the right moment He steps in and proves Himself as our faithful heavenly Father.

CHARLES R. SWINDOLL

Windows of the Soul

Open wide the windows of our spirits and fill us full of light; open wide the door of our hearts that we may receive and entertain Thee with all the powers of our adoration.

Christina Rossetti

Just as there comes a warm sunbeam into every cottage window, so comes a love—born of God's care for every separate need.

Nathaniel Hawthorne

Let there be many windows in your soul, That all the glory of the universe may beautify it.

Ella Wheeler Wilcox

Faith goes up the stairs that love has made and looks out the window which hope has opened.

Charles H. Spurgeon

Day-to-day living becomes a window through which we get a glimpse of life eternal. The eternal illuminates and gives focus to the daily.

Janice Riggle Huie

Windows of the Soul

All the earth shall be filled with the glory of the Lord.

NUMBERS 14:21 NKJV

Glorious Riches

I pray that out of His glorious riches
He may strengthen you with power through
His Spirit in your inner being, so that
Christ may dwell in your hearts through faith.
And I pray that you,
being rooted and established in love,
may have power, together with all the saints,
to grasp how wide and long and high and deep
is the love of Christ,
and to know this love that surpasses knowledge—
that you may be filled to the measure
of all the fullness of God.
Now to Him who is able to do immeasurably more
than all we ask or imagine,
according to His power that is at work within us,
to Him be glory in the church
and in Christ Jesus throughout all generations,
for ever and ever! Amen.

Ephesians 3:16-21 NIV

Glorious Riches

Lord...give me only Your love and Your grace. With this I am rich enough, and I have no more to ask.

IGNATIUS OF LOYOLA

Joy Comes from Within

Joy cannot be pursued. It comes from within. It is a
state of being. It does not depend on circumstances,
but triumphs over circumstances. It produces a
gentleness of spirit and a magnetic personality.

Billy Graham

The God of the universe—the One who created
everything and holds it all in His hands—created each
of us in His image, to bear His likeness, His imprint.
It is only when Christ dwells within our hearts, radiating
the pure light of His love through our humanity that
we discover who we are and what we were intended to be.
There is no other joy that reaches as deep or as wide or
as high—there is no other joy that is more complete.

Joy Comes from Within

The Lord has filled my heart with joy.

1 SAMUEL 2:1 NCV

Special Plans

This is the real gift: you have been given the breath of life, designed with a unique, one-of-a-kind soul that exists forever—the way that you choose to live it doesn't change the fact that you've been given the gift of being now and forever. Priceless in value, you are handcrafted by God, who has a personal design and plan for each of us.

May God's love guide you through the special plans He has for your life.

Allow your dreams a place in your prayers and plans. God-given dreams can help you move into the future He is preparing for you.

Special Plans

....

....

....

....

....

....

....

....

....

....

....

....

....

....

The Lord will work out His plans for my life—for Your faithful love,
O Lord, endures forever.

PSALM 138:8 NLT

The Majesty of God

Honor and majesty surround Him;
strength and beauty fill His sanctuary.

Psalm 96:6 NLT

O Lord, our Lord,
how majestic is Your name in all the earth!
You have set Your glory
above the heavens....
When I consider Your heavens,
the work of Your fingers,
the moon and the stars,
which You have set in place,
what is man that You are mindful of him,
the son of man that You care for him?
You made him a little lower than the heavenly beings
and crowned him with glory and honor....
O Lord, our Lord,
how majestic is Your name in all the earth!

Psalm 8:1, 3-5, 9 NIV

The Majesty of God

....
....
....
....
....
....
....
....
....
....
....
....
....
....
....
....
....
....
....
....

It was God who first set the stars in space; He is their Maker and Master—
they are all in His hands and subject to His will. Such are His power
and His majesty. Behold your God!

J. I. PACKER

Endless Energy, Boundless Strength!

Think excitement, talk excitement, act out excitement,
and you are bound to become an excited person.
Life will take on a new zest, deeper interest and
greater meaning. You can think, talk and act
yourself into dullness or into monotony or into
unhappiness. By the same process you can build up
inspiration, excitement and a surging depth of joy.

Norman Vincent Peale

Hope floods my heart with delight!
Running on air, mad with life, dizzy, reeling,
Upward I mount—faith is sight, life is feeling,
Hope is the day-star of might!

Margaret Witter Fuller

God's holy beauty comes near you, like a spiritual scent,
and it stirs your drowsing soul.... He creates
in you the desire to find Him and run after Him—
to follow wherever He leads you, and to press
peacefully against His heart wherever He is.

John of the Cross

Endless Energy, Boundless Strength!

....

....

....

....

....

....

....

....

....

....

....

....

....

....

....

....

Oh, the utter extravagance of His work in us who trust Him—
endless energy, boundless strength!

EPHESIANS 1:19 THE MESSAGE

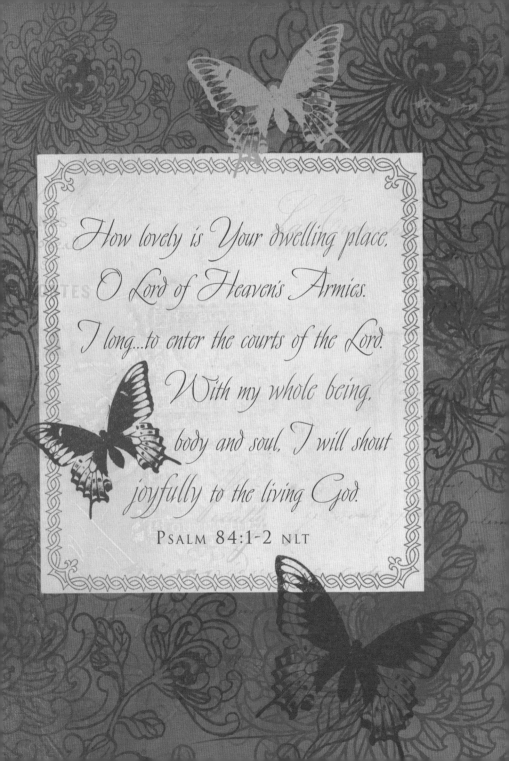

How lovely is Your dwelling place,
O Lord of Heaven's Armies.
I long...to enter the courts of the Lord.
With my whole being,
body and soul, I will shout
joyfully to the living God.

PSALM 84:1-2 NLT

God Is Everywhere

There's not a tint that paints the rose
Or decks the lily fair,
Or marks the humblest flower that grows,
But God has placed it there....
There's not a place on earth's vast round,
In ocean's deep or air,
Where love and beauty are not found,
For God is everywhere.

Lord, give me an open heart to find You everywhere,
to glimpse the heaven enfolded in a bud, and to
experience eternity in the smallest act of love.

Mother Teresa

You already know that God is everywhere....
And where God is, there is heaven—*heaven!*
where His Majesty reigns in glory.

Teresa of Avila

God Is Everywhere

My Presence shall go with you, and I will give you rest.

EXODUS 33:14 NASB

Delight in the Lord

Take delight in the Lord, and He will give you your
heart's desires. Commit everything you do to
the Lord. Trust Him, and He will help you. He will
make your innocence radiate like the dawn, and the
justice of your cause will shine like the noonday sun.

Psalm 37:4-6 NLT

Send forth Your light and Your truth,
let them guide me;
let them bring me to Your holy mountain,
to the place where You dwell.
Then will I go to the altar of God,
to God, my joy and my delight.

Psalm 43:3-4 NIV

Delight in the Lord

Our fulfillment comes in knowing God's glory,
loving Him for it, and delighting in it.

A True Friend

A good friend will sharpen your character,
draw your soul into the light, and challenge
your heart to love in a greater way.

A true friend is distinguished in the crisis of hazard
and necessity; when the gallantry of her aid may show
the worth of her soul and the loyalty of her heart.

Quintus Ennius

'Tis the human touch in this world that counts,
The touch of your hand and mine,
Which means far more to the fainting heart
Than shelter and bread and wine;
For shelter is gone when the night is o'er,
And bread lasts only a day,
But the touch of the hand and the sound of the voice
Sing on in the soul always.

Spencer Michael Free

A True Friend

The right word at the right time is like a custom-made piece of jewelry, and a wise friend's timely reprimand is like a gold ring slipped on your finger. Reliable friends who do what they say are like cool drinks in sweltering heat—refreshing!

PROVERBS 25:11-13 THE MESSAGE

New Every Morning

Morning has broken like the first morning,
Blackbird has spoken like the first bird....
Praise with elation, praise every morning,
God's re-creation of the new day!

Eleanor Farjeon

Today is a new day. You will get out of it just what you put into it. If you have made mistakes, even serious mistakes, there is always another chance for you.... You may have a fresh start any moment you choose, for this thing we call "failure" is not the falling down, but the staying down.

Mary Pickford

That is God's call to us—simply to be people who are content to live close to Him and to renew the kind of life in which the closeness is felt and experienced.

Thomas Merton

New Every Morning

It is good to give thanks to the Lord and to sing praises to Your name, O Most High; to declare Your lovingkindness in the morning and Your faithfulness by night.

PSALM 92:1-2 NASB

New Creation

One man died for everyone. That puts everyone in the
same boat. He included everyone in His death so that
everyone could also be included in His life, a resurrection
life, a far better life than people ever lived on their own.
Because of this decision we don't evaluate people by what
they have or how they look.... Now we look inside,
and what we see is that anyone united with the Messiah
gets a fresh start, is created new. The old life is gone;
a new life burgeons! Look at it! All this comes from the God
who settled the relationship between us and Him, and then
called us to settle our relationships with each other.

2 Corinthians 5:14-18 THE MESSAGE

Forget the former things; do not dwell on the past.
See, I am doing a new thing!

Isaiah 43:18 NIV

New Creation

Always new. Always exciting. Always full of promise.
The mornings of our lives, each a personal daily miracle!

GLORIA GAITHER

Ah, There You Are!

To appreciate beauty; to find the best in others; to give one's self; to leave the world a little better, whether by a healthy child, a garden patch, or a redeemed social condition; to have played and laughed with enthusiasm, and sung with exultation; to know even one life has breathed easier because you have lived...This is to have succeeded.

Ralph Waldo Emerson

There are two kinds of people in the world: those who come into a room and say, "Here I am!" and those who come in and say, "Ah, there you are!"

The blossom cannot tell what becomes of its fragrance as it drifts away, just as no person can tell what becomes of their influence as they continue through life.

Ah, There You Are!

The kingdom of God is...righteousness and peace and joy in the Holy Spirit.... So then we pursue the things which make for peace and the building up of one another.

ROMANS 14:17-19 NASB

A Garland of Grace

Take this to heart. Do what I tell you—live!
Sell everything and buy Wisdom! Forage for Understanding!
Don't forget one word! Don't deviate an inch!
Never walk away from Wisdom—she guards
your life; love her—she keeps her eye on you.
Above all and before all, do this: Get Wisdom!
Write this at the top of your list: Get Understanding!
Throw your arms around her—believe me,
you won't regret it; never let her go—she'll make
your life glorious. She'll garland your life with grace,
she'll festoon your days with beauty.

Proverbs 4:4-9 THE MESSAGE

You no longer live under the requirements of the law.
Instead, you live under the freedom of God's grace.

Romans 6:14 NLT

A Garland of Grace

....
....
....
....
....
....
....
....
....
....
....
....
....
....

I want first of all...to be at peace with myself. I want a singleness of eye, a purity of intention, a central core to my life.... I want, in fact—to borrow from the language of the saints—to live "in grace" as much of the time as possible.

ANNE MORROW LINDBERG

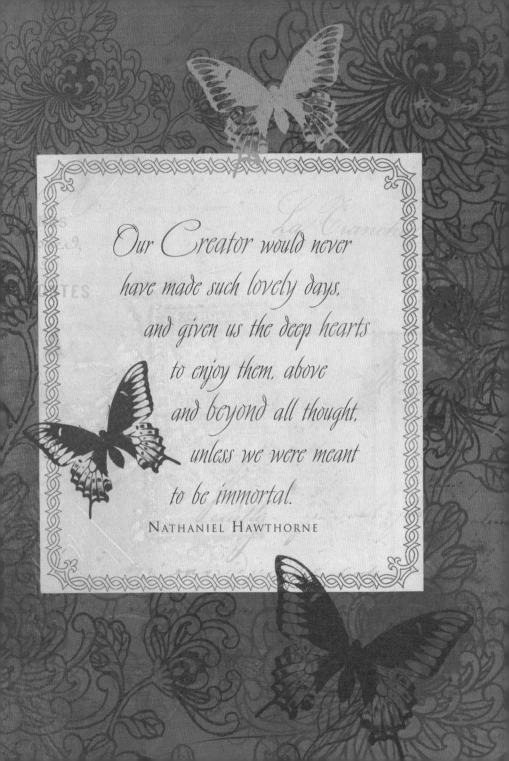

Our Creator would never
have made such lovely days,
and given us the deep hearts
to enjoy them, above
and beyond all thought,
unless we were meant
to be immortal.

NATHANIEL HAWTHORNE

The Wonder of Living

We need to recapture the power of imagination;
we shall find that life can be full of wonder,
mystery, beauty, and joy.

Sir Harold Spencer Jones

When I need a dose of wonder I wait for a clear night
and go look for the stars.... In the country the great
river of the Milky Way streams across the sky,
and I know that our planet is a small part of that
river of stars.... Often the wonder of the stars is
enough to return me to God's loving grace.

Madeleine L'Engle

The wonder of living is held within the beauty
of silence, the glory of sunlight...the sweetness of
fresh spring air, the quiet strength of earth,
and the love that lies at the very root of all things.

The Wonder of Living

Fear Not

Don't be afraid, I've redeemed you.
I've called your name.
You're Mine.
When you're in over your head,
I'll be there with you.
When you're in rough waters,
you will not go down.
When you're between a rock and a hard place,
it won't be a dead end—
Because I am God, your personal God,
The Holy of Israel, your Savior.
I paid a huge price for you...!
That's how much you mean to Me!
That's how much I love you!

Isaiah 43:1-4 THE MESSAGE

If God is for us, who can be against us?

Romans 8:31 NKJV

Fear Not

Nothing we can do will make the Father love us less; nothing we do can make Him love us more. He loves us unconditionally with an everlasting love.

NANCIE CARMICHAEL

My Daily Creed

Let me be a little kinder,
Let me be a little blinder
To the faults of those about me;
Let me praise a little more.
Let me be, when I am weary,
Just a little bit more cheery;
Let me serve a little better
Those that I am striving for.

Let me be a little braver
When temptation bids me waver;
Let me strive a little harder
To be all that I should be.
Let me be a little meeker
With my brother who is weaker;
Let me think more of my neighbor
And a little less of me.

My Daily Creed

Be kind to one other, tender-hearted, forgiving each another,
just as God in Christ also has forgiven you.

EPHESIANS 4:32 NASB

Love Never Fails

If I speak with the tongues of men and of angels,
but do not have love, I have become
a noisy gong or a clanging cymbal.
If I have the gift of prophecy, and know all mysteries
and all knowledge; and if I have all faith,
so as to remove mountains, but do not have love,
I am nothing.
And if I give all my possessions to feed the poor,
and if I surrender my body to be burned,
but do not have love, it profits me nothing.
Love is patient, love is kind and is not jealous;
love does not brag and is not arrogant,
does not act unbecomingly; it does not seek its own,
is not provoked, does not take into account
a wrong suffered, does not rejoice in unrighteousness,
but rejoices with the truth;
bears all things, believes all things,
hopes all things, endures all things.
Love never fails.

1 Corinthians 13:1-8 NASB

Love Never Fails

....

....

....

....

....

....

....

....

....

....

....

....

....

....

An instant of pure love is more precious to God...
than all other good works together.

JOHN OF THE CROSS

God's Passion for You

God is the shepherd in search of His lamb. His legs are scratched, His feet are sore and His eyes are burning. He scales the cliffs and traverses the fields. He explores the caves. He cups His hands to His mouth and calls into the canyon. And the name He calls is yours.

In extravagance of soul we seek His face. In generosity of heart, we glean His gentle touch. In excessiveness of spirit, we love Him and His love comes back to us a hundredfold.

Tricia McCary Rhodes

God's Passion for You

He will feed His flock like a shepherd; He will gather the lambs with His arm, and carry them in His bosom, and gently lead those who are with young.

ISAIAH 40:11 NKJV

Praise Overflows

All enjoyment spontaneously overflows into praise....
The world rings with praise.... I think we delight to praise
what we enjoy because the praise not merely expresses but
completes the enjoyment; it is the appointed consummation.

C. S. Lewis

Does not all nature around me praise God?
If I were silent, I should be an exception to the universe.
Does not the thunder praise Him as it rolls like drums
in the march of the God of armies?... Does not the
lightning write His name in letters of fire? Has not
the whole earth a voice? And...can I silent be?

Charles H. Spurgeon

God's pursuit of praise from us and our pursuit of
pleasure in Him are one and the same pursuit.
God's quest to be glorified and our quest to be
satisfied reach their goal in this one experience:
our delight in God which overflows in praise.

John Piper

Praise Overflows

....

....

....

....

....

....

....

....

....

....

....

....

....

....

O sing to the Lord a new song! Sing to the Lord, all the earth.

PSALM 96:1 NKJV

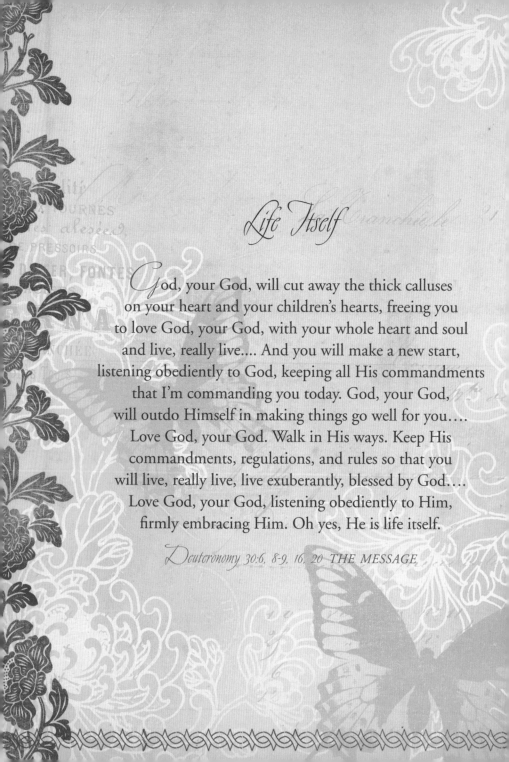

Life Itself

God, your God, will cut away the thick calluses
on your heart and your children's hearts, freeing you
to love God, your God, with your whole heart and soul
and live, really live.... And you will make a new start,
listening obediently to God, keeping all His commandments
that I'm commanding you today. God, your God,
will outdo Himself in making things go well for you....
Love God, your God. Walk in His ways. Keep His
commandments, regulations, and rules so that you
will live, really live, live exuberantly, blessed by God....
Love God, your God, listening obediently to Him,
firmly embracing Him. Oh yes, He is life itself.

Deuteronomy 30:6, 8-9, 16, 20 THE MESSAGE

Life Itself

....
....
....
....
....
....
....
....
....
....
....
....
....
....

I asked God for all things that I might enjoy life.
He gave me life that I might enjoy all things.

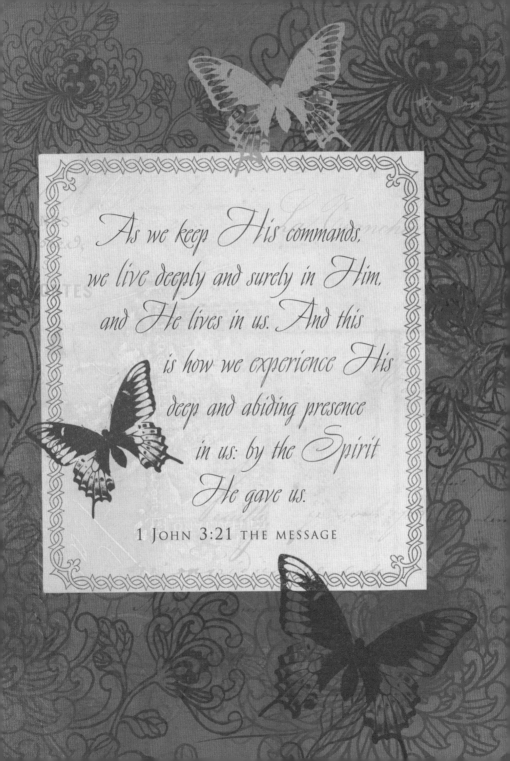

As we keep His commands,
we live deeply and surely in Him,
and He lives in us. And this
is how we experience His
deep and abiding presence
in us: by the Spirit
He gave us.

1 JOHN 3:21 THE MESSAGE

Taking Action

*A*ll the beautiful sentiments in the world weigh
less than a simple lovely action.

James Russell Lowell

*B*eing a woman of God is loving God with all my heart,
soul, mind, and body, and loving my neighbor—actively.

Stacey Lynn Merkt

*E*verybody can be great...because anybody can serve.
You don't have to have a college degree to serve.... You only
need a heart full of grace. A soul generated by love.

Martin Luther King, Jr.

*W*e can never untangle all the woes in other people's
lives. We can't produce miracles overnight.
But we can bring a cup of cool water to a thirsty soul,
or a scoop of laughter to a lonely heart.

Barbara Johnson

Taking Action

Depend on the Lord in whatever you do, and your plans will succeed.

PROVERBS 16:3 NCV

Know that You Are Heard

I call on You, O God, for You will answer me;
give ear to me and hear my prayer.
Show the wonder of Your great love,
You who save by Your right hand
those who take refuge in You.

Psalm 17:6-7 NKJV

I want to look life in the eye....
I've thrown myself headlong into Your arms—
I'm celebrating Your rescue.
I'm singing at the top of my lungs,
I'm so full of answered prayers.

Psalm 13:3, 5-6 THE MESSAGE

Come, let us tell of the Lord's greatness;
let us exalt His name together.
I prayed to the Lord, and He answered me.
He freed me from all my fears.
Those who look to Him for help will be radiant with joy;

Psalm 34:3-5 NLT

Know that You Are Heard

So wait before the Lord. Wait in the stillness. And in that stillness, assurance will come to you. You will know that you are heard;... you will hear quiet words spoken to you yourself, perhaps to your grateful surprise and refreshment.

AMY CARMICHAEL

The Rhythms of Life

*I*n waiting we begin to get in touch with the rhythms of life—stillness and action, listening and decision. They are the rhythms of God. It is in the everyday and the commonplace that we learn patience, acceptance, and contentment.

Richard J. Foster

*L*ove comes while we rest against our Father's chest. Joy comes when we catch the rhythms of His heart. Peace comes when we live in harmony with those rhythms.

Ken Gire

*G*od knows the rhythm of my spirit and knows my heart thoughts. He is as close as breathing.

The Rhythms of Life

....

....

....

....

....

....

....

....

....

....

....

....

....

*How can we honor our God with our lives, the God who gives rain in
both spring and autumn and maintains the rhythm of the seasons?*

JEREMIAH 5:24 THE MESSAGE

Go Out with Joy

So you will go out with joy and be led out in peace.
The mountains and hills will burst into song before you,
and all the trees in the fields will clap their hands....
These things will be a reminder of the Lord's promise.

Isaiah 55:12 NCV

But let all who take refuge in You rejoice; let them
sing joyful praises forever. Spread Your protection
over them, that all who love Your name may be filled
with joy. For You bless the godly, O Lord;
You surround them with Your shield of love.

Psalm 5:11-12 NLT

Go Out with Joy

Those who run in the path of God's commands
have their hearts set free.

Love Intensified

Love makes burdens lighter, because you divide them.
It makes joys more intense, because you share them.
It makes you stronger, so that you can reach out and become
involved with life in ways you dared not risk alone.

Love each other as God loves you,
with an intense and particular love.

Mother Teresa

We never live so intensely as when we love strongly.
We never realize ourselves so vividly as when we are
in the full glow of love for others.

Walter Rauschenbusch

Love Intensified

....

....

....

....

....

....

....

....

....

....

....

....

....

....

Go after a life of love as if your life depended on it—because it does.
Give yourselves to the gifts God gives you. Most of all, try to proclaim His truth.

1 Corinthians 14:1 the message

To Be Alive

How beautiful it is to be alive!
To wake each morn as if the Maker's grace
Did us afresh from nothingness derive,
That we might sing "How happy is our case!
How beautiful it is to be alive."

Henry Septimus Sutton

It seems to me we can never give up longing and wishing while we are alive. There are certain things we feel to be beautiful and good, and we must hunger for them.

George Eliot

Isn't it splendid to think of all the things there are to find out about? It just makes me feel glad to be alive— it's such an interesting world. It wouldn't be half so interesting if we knew all about everything.

Lucy Maud Montgomery

To Be Alive

....

....

....

....

....

....

....

....

....

....

....

....

....

....

The Lord will command His lovingkindness in the daytime; and His song will be with me in the night, a prayer to the God of my life.

PSALM 42:8 NASB

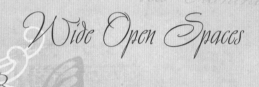

Wide Open Spaces

By entering through faith into what God has
always wanted to do for us—set us right with Him,
make us fit for Him—we have it all together with God
because of our Master Jesus. And that's not all:
We throw open our doors to God and discover at the
same moment that He has already thrown open His door
to us. We find ourselves standing where we always hoped
we might stand—out in the wide open spaces of God's
grace and glory, standing tall and shouting our praise.

Romans 5:1-2 THE MESSAGE

Wide Open Spaces

....

....

....

....

....

....

....

....

....

....

....

....

....

....

Whoever walks toward God one step,
God runs toward him two.

Take time to notice all the
usually unnoticed, simple things
in life. Delight in
the never-ending hope
that's available
every day!

The Fullness of Life

Contentment comes as the infallible result of great acceptances, great humilities—of not trying to make ourselves this or that, but of surrendering ourselves to the fullness of life—of letting life flow through us.

David Grayson

Gratitude unlocks the fullness of life. It turns what we have into enough, and more.... It can turn a meal into a feast, a house into a home, a stranger into a friend. It turns problems into gifts, failures into successes, the unexpected into perfect timing, and mistakes into important events.

Melody Beattie

I think what we're longing for is not "the good life" as it's been advertised to us in the American dream, but life in its fullness, its richness, its abundance. Living more reflectively helps us enter into that fullness.

Ken Gire

The Fullness of Life

You will show me the path of life; in Your presence is fullness of joy; at Your right hand are pleasures forevermore.

PSALM 16:11 NKJV

Delight in His Creation

In the beginning God created the heavens
and the earth.... Then God saw everything that
He had made, and indeed it was very good.

Genesis 1:1, 31 NKJV

For since the creation of the world God's
invisible qualities—His eternal power and
divine nature—have been clearly seen,
being understood from what has been made.

Romans 1:20 NIV

God stretches the northern sky over empty space and
hangs the earth on nothing. He wraps the rain in His thick
clouds, and the clouds don't burst with the weight.
He covers the face of the moon, shrouding it with His
clouds. He created the horizon when He separated the
waters; He set the boundary between day and night....
His Spirit made the heavens beautiful, and His power
pierced the gliding serpent. These are just the beginning
of all that He does, merely a whisper of His power.
Who, then, can comprehend the thunder of His power?

Job 26:7-10, 12-14 NLT

Delight in His Creation

Nature has been for me, for as long as I can remember, a source of solace, inspiration, adventure, and delight.

Indescribable Love

Could we with ink the ocean fill,
And were the skies of parchment made,
Were every stalk on earth a quill,
And every man a scribe by trade
To write the love of God above
Would drain the ocean dry,
Nor could the scroll contain the whole
Though stretched from sky to sky.

Meir Ben Isaac Nehorai

Love is the response of the heart to the
overwhelming goodness of God....
You may be so awestruck and full of love at
His presence that words do not come.

Richard J. Foster

Indescribable Love

....

....

....

....

....

....

....

....

....

....

....

....

....

....

Thanks be to God for His indescribable gift!

2 Corinthians 9:15 NASB

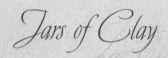

Jars of Clay

*B*ut thanks be to God, who always leads us in
triumphal procession in Christ and through us spreads
everywhere the fragrance of the knowledge of Him.
For we are to God the aroma of Christ among those
who are being saved and those who are perishing.

2 Corinthians 2:14-15 NIV

*F*or God, who said, "Let there be light in the darkness,"
has made this light shine in our hearts so we could know
the glory of God that is seen in the face of Jesus Christ.
We now have this light shining in our hearts,
but we ourselves are like fragile clay jars containing
this great treasure. This makes it clear that our great
power is from God, not from ourselves.

2 Corinthians 4:6-7 NLT

Jars of Clay

....

....

....

....

....

....

....

....

....

....

....

....

....

....

....

*Lord, help me to spread Your fragrance everywhere I go, and may
Your radiant light be visible through me.*

Learning to Dance

You changed my sorrow into dancing.
You took away my clothes of sadness,
    and clothed me in happiness.
I will sing to You and not be silent.
Lord, my God, I will praise You forever.

Psalm 30:11-12 NCV

*P*raise God in His sanctuary;
    praise Him in His mighty heaven!
Praise Him for His mighty works;
    praise His unequaled greatness!...
    praise Him with the lyre and harp!
Praise Him with the tambourine and dancing;
    praise Him with strings and flutes!
Praise Him with a clash of cymbals;...
Let everything that breathes sing praises to the Lord!

Psalm 150:1-2, 4-6 NLT

Learning to Dance

....

....

....

....

....

....

....

....

....

....

....

....

....

Let God have you, and let God love you—and don't be surprised if your heart begins to hear music you've never heard and your feet learn to dance as never before.

MAX LUCADO

Your Presence in the World

Every person ever created is so special that their presence in the world makes it richer and fuller and more wonderful than it could ever have been without them.

We were not sent into this world to do anything into which we cannot put our hearts.

John Ruskin

Use what talents you possess: the woods would be very silent if no birds sang there except those that sang best.

Henry van Dyke

God gives everyone a special gift and a special place to use it.

Your Presence in the World

....

....

....

....

....

....

....

....

....

....

....

....

....

Where you are right now is God's place for you.
Live and obey and love and believe right there.

1 CORINTHIANS 7:17 THE MESSAGE

Abundant Life

I came to give life—life in all its fullness. I am the good shepherd. The good shepherd gives His life for the sheep.

John 10:10-11 NCV

In the beginning was the Word, and the Word was with God, and the Word was God. He was in the beginning with God. All things came into being through Him, and apart from Him nothing came into being that has come into being. In Him was life, and the life was the Light of men.

John 1:1-4 NASB

Abundant Life

....

....

....

....

....

....

....

....

....

....

....

....

....

....

....

He is looking for people who will come in simple dependence upon His grace....
At this very moment, He's looking at you.

JACK HAYFORD

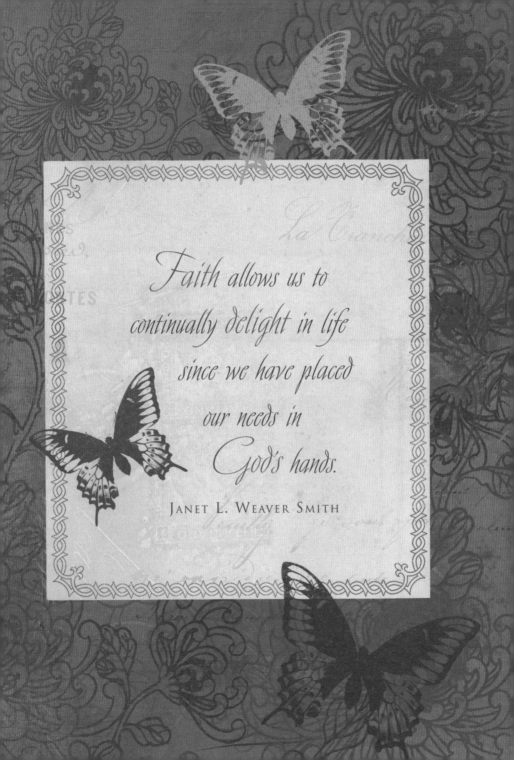

Faith allows us to
continually delight in life
since we have placed
our needs in
God's hands.

JANET L. WEAVER SMITH

God Give Me Joy

God give me joy in the common things:
In the dawn that lures, the eve that sings.
In the new grass sparkling after rain,
In the late wind's wild and weird refrain;
In the springtime's spacious field of gold,
In the precious light by winter doled.

God give me joy in the love of friends,
In the dear home talk as summer ends;
In the songs of children, unrestrained;
In the sober wisdom age has gained.

God give me joy in the tasks that press,
In the memories that burn and bless;
In the thought that life has love to spend,
In the faith that God's at journey's end.
God give me hope for each day that springs,
God give me joy in the common things!

Thomas Curtis Clark

God Give Me Joy

....
....
....
....
....
....
....
....
....
....
....
....
....
....
....
....

The Lord is my strength and shield. I trust Him with all my heart. He helps me, and my heart is filled with joy. I burst out in songs of thanksgiving.

PSALM 28:7 NLT

An Undivided Heart

Above all else, guard your heart,
for it is the wellspring of life.

Proverbs 4:23 NIV

I will give them an undivided heart and put a
new spirit in them; I will remove from them their
heart of stone and give them a heart of flesh. Then…
they will be my people, and I will be their God.

Ezekiel 11:19-20 NIV

"Love the Lord your God with all your heart,
all your soul, and all your mind."
This is the first and greatest commandment.

Matthew 22:37-38 NLT

An Undivided Heart

....
....
....
....
....
....
....
....
....
....
....
....
....
....
....

In the deepest heart of everyone, God planted a longing for
Himself as He is: a God of love.

EUGENIA PRICE

Glorious Handiwork

*H*e made you so you could share in His creation,
could love and laugh and know Him.

Ted Griffen

*Y*ou are a creation of God unequaled anywhere in the
universe.... Thank Him for yourself and then for
all the rest of His glorious handiwork.

Norman Vincent Peale

*T*he huge dome of the sky is of all things sensuously
perceived the most like infinity. When God made space and
worlds that move in space, and clothed our world with air,
and gave us such eyes and such imaginations as those
we have, He knew what the sky would mean to us....
We cannot be certain that this was not indeed one of
the chief purposes for which Nature was created.

C. S. Lewis

Glorious Handiwork

....

....

....

....

....

....

....

....

....

....

....

....

....

....

....

....

The heavens declare His righteousness, and all the peoples see His glory.

PSALM 97:6 NKJV

An Inspiration to Love

We always thank God for all of you, mentioning you in our prayers. We continually remember before our God and Father your work produced by faith, your labor prompted by love, and your endurance inspired by hope in our Lord Jesus Christ.

1 Thessalonians 1:2-3 NIV

Does your life in Christ give you strength? Does His love comfort you? Do we share together in the spirit? Do you have mercy and kindness? If so, make me very happy by having the same thoughts, sharing the same love, and having one mind and purpose.

Philippians 2:1-2 NCV

An Inspiration to Love

....

....

....

....

....

....

....

....

....

....

....

....

....

....

*Look deep within yourself and recognize what brings life and grace into
your heart. It is this that can be shared with those around you.
You are loved by God. This is an inspiration to love.*

CHRISTOPHER DE VINCK

Satisfied

In comparison with this big world, the human heart is only a small thing. Though the world is so large, it is utterly unable to satisfy this tiny heart. Our ever growing soul and its capacities can be satisfied only in the infinite God. As water is restless until it reaches its level, so the soul has no peace until it rests in God.

Sadhu Sundar Singh

You have set Your glory above the heavens.
Thy glory flames from sun and star:
Center and soul of every sphere,
Yet to each loving heart how near.

Oliver Wendell Holmes

God bless you and utterly satisfy your heart...
with Himself.

Amy Carmichael

Satisfied

He is Lord of heaven and earth.... He Himself gives life and
breath to everything, and He satisfies every need.

ACTS 17:24-25

It's usually through our hard times,

the *unexpected* and not-according-to-plan times,

that we experience God in more intimate ways.

We discover an *unquenchable* longing

to know Him more.

It's a *passion*...that pursues God

and knows He is relentless in *His* pursuit

of each one of us.